Contents

Building the ×2 table	4
Multiplying by 2	5
Dividing by 2	6
Multiplying and dividing by 2	8
Solving problems	10
Building the ×5 table	11
Multiplying by 5	12
Dividing by 5	13
Multiplying and dividing by 5	15
Using ×5 table facts	16
Solving problems	17
Multiplying and dividing by 2 and 5	18
Building the ×10 table	19
Multiplying by 10	20
Dividing by 10	21
Multiplying and dividing by 10	23
Using ×10 table facts	24
Solving problems	25
Solving mixed problems	26
Building the ×3 table	27
Multiplying by 3	28
Dividing by 3	29
Multiplying and dividing by 3	31
Using ×3 table facts	32
Solving problems	33
Multiplying and dividing by 2, 3, 5 and 10	34
Building the ×4 table	35
Multiplying by 4	36
Dividing by 4	37
Multiplying and dividing by 4	39
Using ×4 table facts	40
Solving problems	41
Multiplying and dividing by 3 and 4	42
Solving mixed problems	44
What I know	46
Multiplication table	47

Building the ×2 table

Read the numbers on the trains below. Count in **2**s.

Fill in the missing numbers.

Fill in the answers. Each answer goes in the box by the question.

Use the pennies to help you count the two sets. Then write the total.

1 + 1 = ☐   **1** times **2** is ☐

2 + 2 = ☐   **2** times **2** is ☐

3 + 3 = ☐   **3** times **2** is ☐

4 + 4 = ☐   **4** times **2** is ☐

5 + 5 = ☐   **5** times **2** is ☐

6 + 6 = ☐   **6** times **2** is ☐

7 + 7 = ☐   **7** times **2** is ☐

8 + 8 = ☐   **8** times **2** is ☐

9 + 9 = ☐   **9** times **2** is ☐

10 + 10 = ☐   **10** times **2** is ☐

11 + 11 = ☐   **11** times **2** is ☐

12 + 12 = ☐   **12** times **2** is ☐

Multiplying by 2

Write the answers to the ×2 table.

Each answer goes in the box by the question.

1 × 2 = ☐

2 × 2 = ☐

3 × 2 = ☐

4 × 2 = ☐

5 × 2 = ☐

6 × 2 = ☐

7 × 2 = ☐

8 × 2 = ☐

9 × 2 = ☐

10 × 2 = ☐

11 × 2 = ☐

12 × 2 = ☐

You have just written the ×2 table chart.

Write the answers on the ×2 train tickets.

If you need help, look at the ×2 table chart.

5 × 2 = ☐

6 × ☐ = 12

9 × 2 = ☐

7 × ☐ = 14

4 × ☐ = 8

10 × 2 = ☐

12 × 2 = ☐

Dividing by 2

Share the spots between the leopards. Write the answers. Try drawing the spots to help you.

2 spots shared between **2** leopards

2 divided by **2** is ☐
2 ÷ 2 = ☐

4 spots shared between **2** leopards

4 divided by **2** is ☐
4 ÷ 2 = ☐

6 spots shared between **2** leopards

6 divided by **2** is ☐
6 ÷ 2 = ☐

8 spots shared between **2** leopards

8 divided by **2** is ☐
8 ÷ 2 = ☐

10 spots shared between **2** leopards

10 divided by **2** is ☐
10 ÷ 2 = ☐

12 spots shared between **2** leopards

12 divided by **2** is ☐
12 ÷ 2 = ☐

14 spots shared between **2** leopards
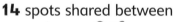
14 divided by **2** is ☐
14 ÷ 2 = ☐

16 spots shared between **2** leopards

16 divided by **2** is ☐
16 ÷ 2 = ☐

18 spots shared between **2** leopards

18 divided by **2** is ☐
18 ÷ 2 = ☐

20 spots shared between **2** leopards

20 divided by **2** is ☐
20 ÷ 2 = ☐

22 spots shared between **2** leopards

22 divided by **2** is ☐
22 ÷ 2 = ☐

24 spots shared between **2** leopards

24 divided by **2** is ☐
24 ÷ 2 = ☐

Dividing by 2

Each monkey has a question. The answer to each question is on a vine leaf.

Draw lines so that the monkeys can reach the answers.

7 11 10 5 2 4 6 3 9 8 12

18 ÷ 2 =

10 ÷ 2 =

14 ÷ 2 =

24 ÷ 2 =

16 ÷ 2 =

12 ÷ 2 =

8 ÷ 2 =

6 ÷ 2 =

20 ÷ 2 =

22 ÷ 2 =

4 ÷ 2 =

One monkey shared **16** bananas equally with her brother.

How many bananas did they have each?

Answer:

Multiplying and dividing by 2

You can multiply by **2**. Write the answers. Use the ants to help you.

5 + 5 = ☐   5 × 2 = ☐

2 + 2 + 2 + 2 + 2 = 10
2 × 5 = ☐

7 + 7 = ☐   7 × 2 = ☐

2 + 2 + 2 + 2 + 2 + 2 + 2 = ☐
2 × 7 = ☐

Write the answers to these pairs of multiplications. Use the grasshoppers to help you.

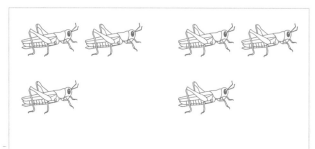

3 × 2 = ☐   2 × 3 = ☐

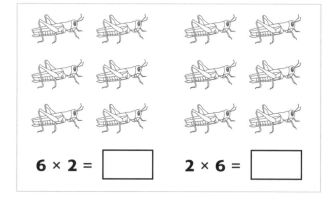

6 × 2 = ☐   2 × 6 = ☐

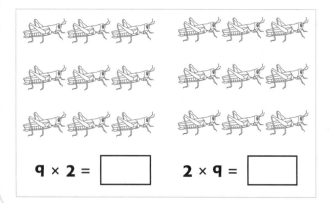

9 × 2 = ☐   2 × 9 = ☐

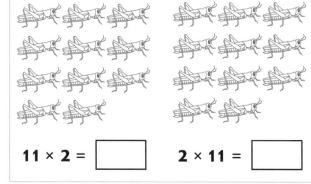

11 × 2 = ☐   2 × 11 = ☐

Schofield & Sims Times Tables Practice 1

Multiplying and dividing by 2

You can divide by **2**. If you know one division fact you can work out another one.

Use the toadstools to help you.

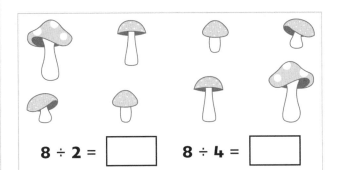

8 ÷ 2 = ☐   8 ÷ 4 = ☐

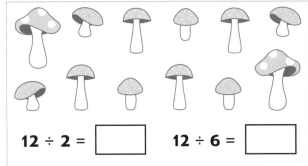

12 ÷ 2 = ☐   12 ÷ 6 = ☐

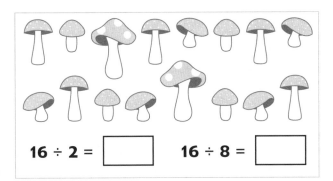

16 ÷ 2 = ☐   16 ÷ 8 = ☐

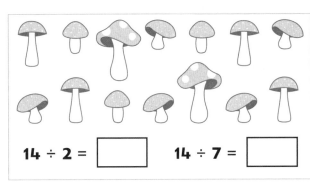

14 ÷ 2 = ☐   14 ÷ 7 = ☐

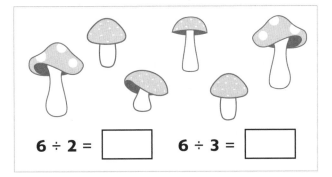

6 ÷ 2 = ☐   6 ÷ 3 = ☐

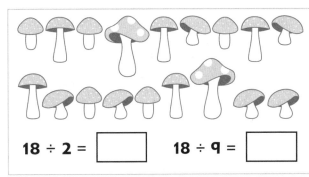

18 ÷ 2 = ☐   18 ÷ 9 = ☐

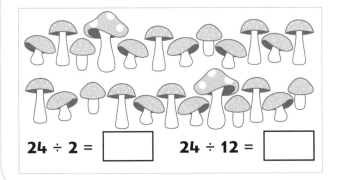

24 ÷ 2 = ☐   24 ÷ 12 = ☐

20 ÷ 2 = ☐   20 ÷ 10 = ☐

Luke shares **12** mushrooms equally with his sister.

How many mushrooms do they have each?   Answer: ☐

Solving problems

Write the answers to these multiplications in the wheel.

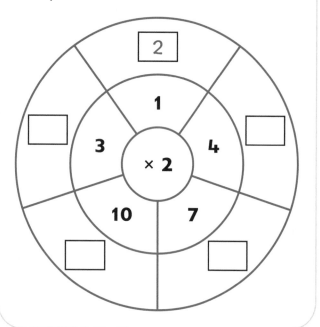

Write the answers to these divisions in the wheel.

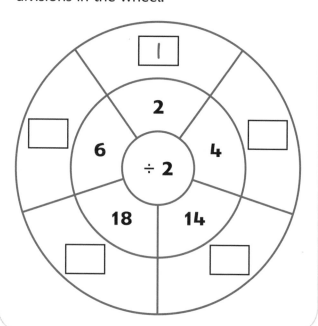

There are **2** bowls of goldfish. Each bowl has **6** goldfish in it. How many goldfish is that in total?

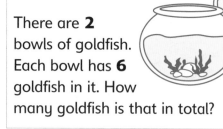

Lily buys **12** boxes of fish food. Each box of fish food has **2** packets in it. How many packets are there altogether?

18 tadpoles are shared between **2** ponds. How many tadpoles are in each pond?

Tom shares **14** rocks equally into **2** buckets. How many rocks are there in each bucket?

14 ROCKS

2 children collect **11** sticks each. How many sticks is that in total?

There are **12** toads and some rocks. **6** toads sit on each rock. How many rocks are needed for the toads?

Building the ×5 table

The frog wants to jump in **5**s along the lily pads. Write the numbers for the frog.

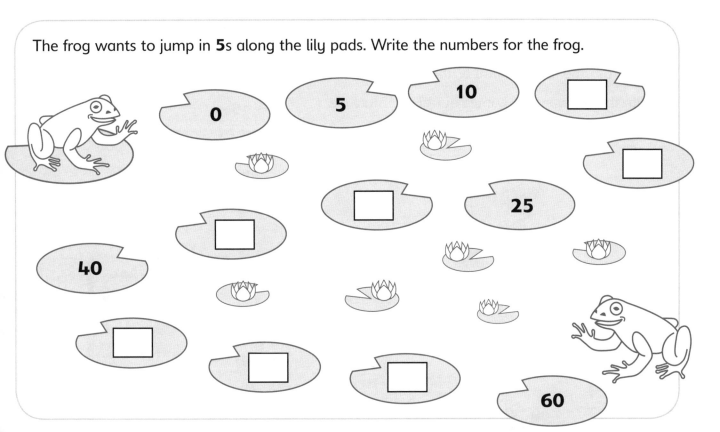

Fill in these answers.

1 + 1 + 1 + 1 + 1 = ☐	**1** times **5** is ☐
2 + 2 + 2 + 2 + 2 = ☐	**2** times **5** is ☐
3 + 3 + 3 + 3 + 3 = ☐	**3** times **5** is ☐
4 + 4 + 4 + 4 + 4 = ☐	**4** times **5** is ☐
5 + 5 + 5 + 5 + 5 = ☐	**5** times **5** is ☐
6 + 6 + 6 + 6 + 6 = ☐	**6** times **5** is ☐
7 + 7 + 7 + 7 + 7 = ☐	**7** times **5** is ☐
8 + 8 + 8 + 8 + 8 = ☐	**8** times **5** is ☐
9 + 9 + 9 + 9 + 9 = ☐	**9** times **5** is ☐
10 + 10 + 10 + 10 + 10 = ☐	**10** times **5** is ☐
11 + 11 + 11 + 11 + 11 = ☐	**11** times **5** is ☐
12 + 12 + 12 + 12 + 12 = ☐	**12** times **5** is ☐

Multiplying by 5

This machine multiplies by **5**.

Read from the list the number that goes into the machine.

Write the answer that comes out of the machine.

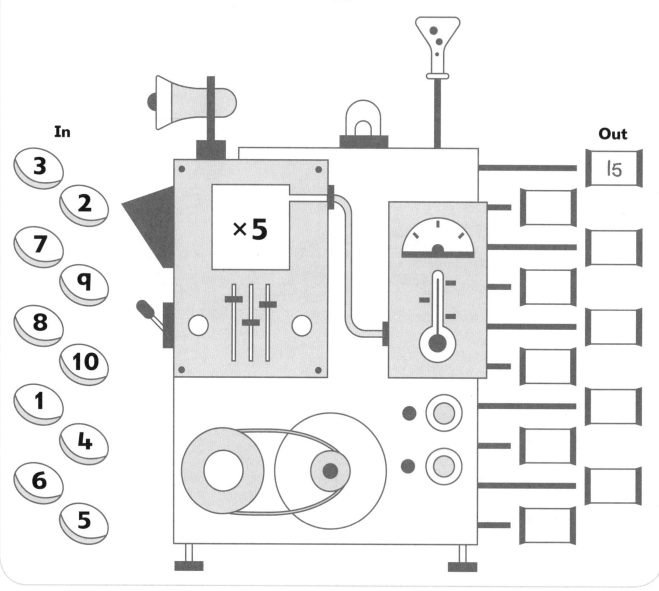

Write the answers to these multiplication sentences.

6 × 5 = ☐   4 × 5 = ☐   10 × 5 = ☐

8 × 5 = ☐   3 × 5 = ☐   2 × 5 = ☐

9 × 5 = ☐   1 × 5 = ☐   7 × 5 = ☐

11 × 5 = ☐   5 × 5 = ☐   12 × 5 = ☐

Dividing by 5

The factory needs to fill **5** bags equally with sweets.

Write how many are in each bag. Try drawing the sweets to help you.

5 sweets shared between **5** bags	**10** sweets shared between **5** bags	**15** sweets shared between **5** bags

5 divided by **5** is ☐ **5 ÷ 5 =** ☐	**10** divided by **5** is ☐ **10 ÷ 5 =** ☐	**15** divided by **5** is ☐ **15 ÷ 5 =** ☐
20 sweets shared between **5** bags	**25** sweets shared between **5** bags	**30** sweets shared between **5** bags

20 divided by **5** is ☐ **20 ÷ 5 =** ☐	**25** divided by **5** is ☐ **25 ÷ 5 =** ☐	**30** divided by **5** is ☐ **30 ÷ 5 =** ☐
35 sweets shared between **5** bags	**40** sweets shared between **5** bags	**45** sweets shared between **5** bags

35 divided by **5** is ☐ **35 ÷ 5 =** ☐	**40** divided by **5** is ☐ **40 ÷ 5 =** ☐	**45** divided by **5** is ☐ **45 ÷ 5 =** ☐
50 sweets shared between **5** bags	**55** sweets shared between **5** bags	**60** sweets shared between **5** bags

50 divided by **5** is ☐ **50 ÷ 5 =** ☐	**55** divided by **5** is ☐ **55 ÷ 5 =** ☐	**60** divided by **5** is ☐ **60 ÷ 5 =** ☐

Dividing by 5

Choose one of the cars and look at the division question written on it.

Find the building with the right answer to the question.

Draw a line from the car to the building which shows the right answer.

Then do the same with the other buildings and cars.

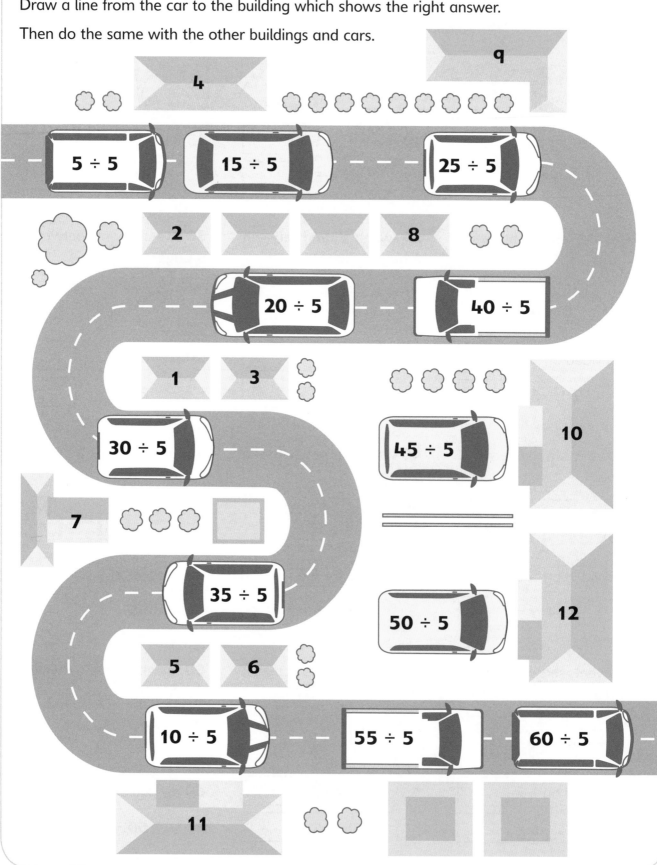

Multiplying and dividing by 5

Write the answers to these multiplications.

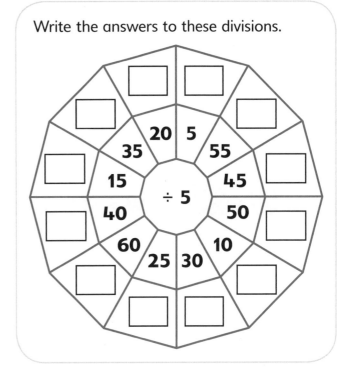

Write the answers to these divisions.

You know these facts...

$4 \times 5 = 20$ $20 \div 5 = 4$

...so you can find these facts!

$5 \times 4 = 20$ $20 \div 4 = 5$

Draw a line from each driver to the correct car.

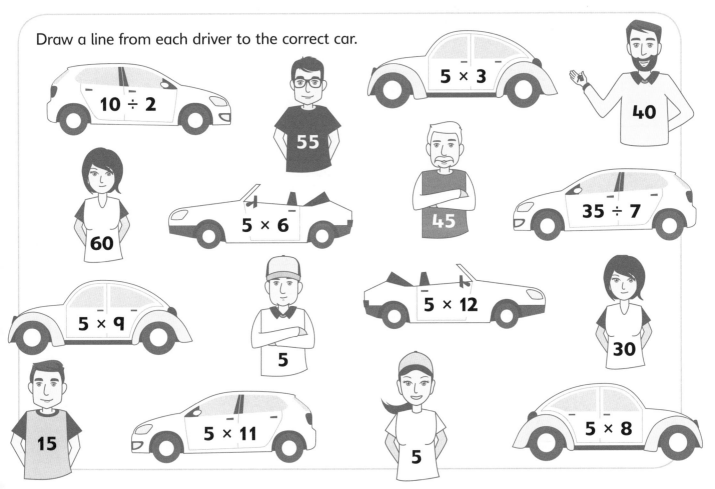

Using ×5 table facts

Choose a number from the shelf to complete each number sentence.

Write the number into the multiplication or division sentence in the basket.

Shelf numbers: 5, 25, 35, 50, 55, 5, 9, 5, 6, 12

$\boxed{} \times 3 = 15$

$\boxed{} \div 5 = 10$

$\boxed{} \times 5 = 45$

$\boxed{} \times 8 = 40$

$\boxed{} \div 5 = 11$

$\boxed{} \times 5 = 60$

$\boxed{} \div 5 = 7$

$\boxed{} \times 4 = 20$

$\boxed{} \div 5 = 5$

$\boxed{} \times 5 = 30$

5p

What will **6** fizzy worms at **5**p each cost?   Answer: $\boxed{}$ p

How much will **10** fizzy worms cost?   Answer: $\boxed{}$ p

Solving problems

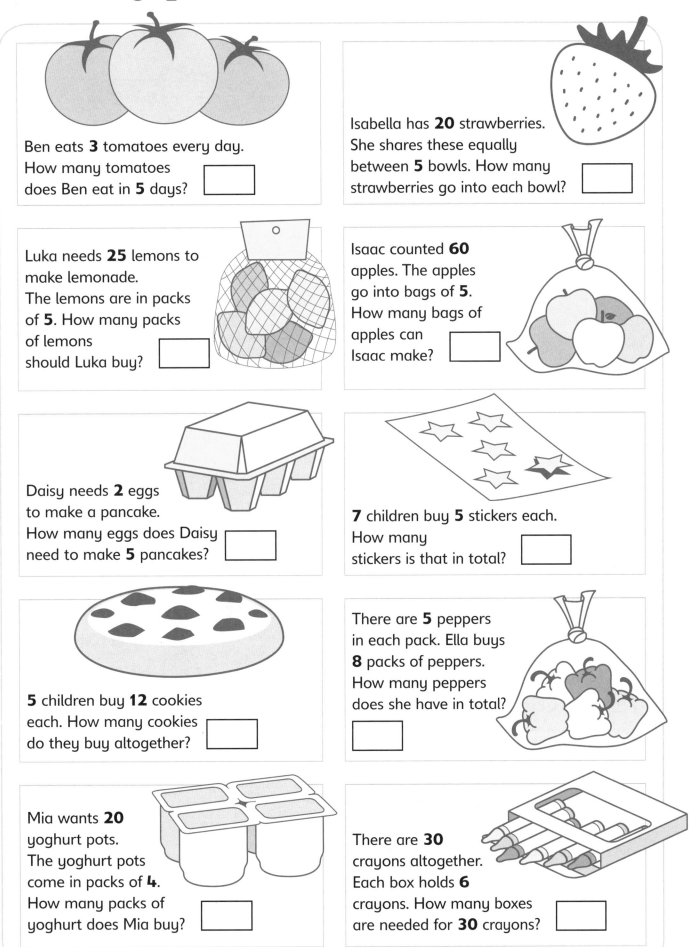

Ben eats **3** tomatoes every day. How many tomatoes does Ben eat in **5** days?

Isabella has **20** strawberries. She shares these equally between **5** bowls. How many strawberries go into each bowl?

Luka needs **25** lemons to make lemonade. The lemons are in packs of **5**. How many packs of lemons should Luka buy?

Isaac counted **60** apples. The apples go into bags of **5**. How many bags of apples can Isaac make?

Daisy needs **2** eggs to make a pancake. How many eggs does Daisy need to make **5** pancakes?

7 children buy **5** stickers each. How many stickers is that in total?

5 children buy **12** cookies each. How many cookies do they buy altogether?

There are **5** peppers in each pack. Ella buys **8** packs of peppers. How many peppers does she have in total?

Mia wants **20** yoghurt pots. The yoghurt pots come in packs of **4**. How many packs of yoghurt does Mia buy?

There are **30** crayons altogether. Each box holds **6** crayons. How many boxes are needed for **30** crayons?

Multiplying and dividing by 2 and 5

Write the answer in the box.

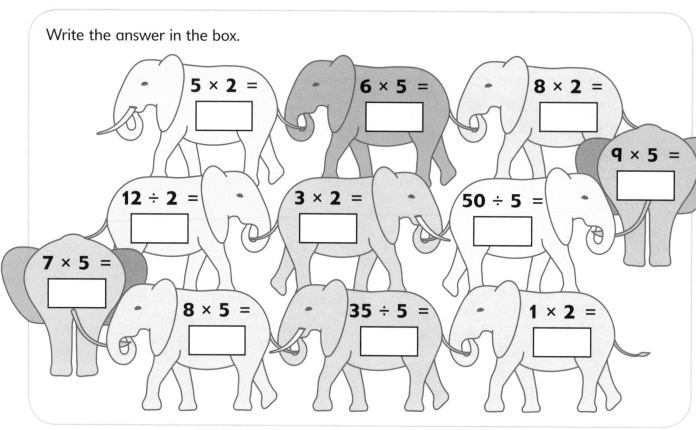

5 × 2 =

6 × 5 =

8 × 2 =

9 × 5 =

12 ÷ 2 =

3 × 2 =

50 ÷ 5 =

7 × 5 =

8 × 5 =

35 ÷ 5 =

1 × 2 =

4 elephants eat 5 cabbages each.

How many cabbages do they eat altogether?

There are 14 elephants.

The same number of elephants sleep
in 2 houses.

How many elephants sleep in each house?

Some of the elephants eat 3 carrots each.

They eat 15 carrots in total.

How many elephants eat the carrots?

There are 30 apples for some of the elephants.

6 elephants share the apples equally
between them.

How many apples does each elephant eat?

There are 2 zookeepers who look after
18 elephants and 4 baby elephants too.

How many elephants does each zookeeper look after?

Building the ×10 table

Count in **10**s. Write the missing numbers.

0   10   20   30   [ ]   [ ]   [ ]   [ ]   80   90   100

[ ]   [ ]   40   50   60   [ ]   [ ]   [ ]   [ ]   [ ]   120

Fill in these answers.

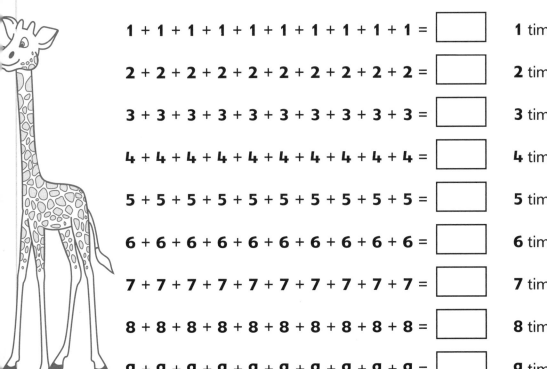

1 + 1 + 1 + 1 + 1 + 1 + 1 + 1 + 1 + 1 = [ ]	**1** times **10** is [ ]
2 + 2 + 2 + 2 + 2 + 2 + 2 + 2 + 2 + 2 = [ ]	**2** times **10** is [ ]
3 + 3 + 3 + 3 + 3 + 3 + 3 + 3 + 3 + 3 = [ ]	**3** times **10** is [ ]
4 + 4 + 4 + 4 + 4 + 4 + 4 + 4 + 4 + 4 = [ ]	**4** times **10** is [ ]
5 + 5 + 5 + 5 + 5 + 5 + 5 + 5 + 5 + 5 = [ ]	**5** times **10** is [ ]
6 + 6 + 6 + 6 + 6 + 6 + 6 + 6 + 6 + 6 = [ ]	**6** times **10** is [ ]
7 + 7 + 7 + 7 + 7 + 7 + 7 + 7 + 7 + 7 = [ ]	**7** times **10** is [ ]
8 + 8 + 8 + 8 + 8 + 8 + 8 + 8 + 8 + 8 = [ ]	**8** times **10** is [ ]
9 + 9 + 9 + 9 + 9 + 9 + 9 + 9 + 9 + 9 = [ ]	**9** times **10** is [ ]
10 + 10 + 10 + 10 + 10 + 10 + 10 + 10 + 10 + 10 = [ ]	**10** times **10** is [ ]
11 + 11 + 11 + 11 + 11 + 11 + 11 + 11 + 11 + 11 = [ ]	**11** times **10** is [ ]
12 + 12 + 12 + 12 + 12 + 12 + 12 + 12 + 12 + 12 = [ ]	**12** times **10** is [ ]

Multiplying by 10

Multiply each number on the bees by **10**.
Draw an arrow to the correct answer.

Bees: 5, 8, 6, 3, 1, 4, 7, 9, 2, 10

×10 (on flower)

Hexagons: 60, 100, 30, 70, 10, 40, 90, 80, 50, 20

Write the answers.

5 × 10 =

8 × 10 =

3 × 10 =

6 × 10 =

1 × 10 =

7 × 10 =

9 × 10 =

10 × 10 =

2 × 10 =

4 × 10 =

11 × 10 =

12 × 10 =

Dividing by 10

Write the answers.

$10 \div 10 =$ ☐

$50 \div 10 =$ ☐

$20 \div 10 =$ ☐

$60 \div 10 =$ ☐

$120 \div 10 =$ ☐

$90 \div 10 =$ ☐

$80 \div 10 =$ ☐

$100 \div 10 =$ ☐

$70 \div 10 =$ ☐

$40 \div 10 =$ ☐

Fill in the missing numbers.

☐   ☐

20   50

☐   40 $\div 10$ 90   ☐

60   80

☐   ☐

Fill in the missing numbers.

6   ☐

☐   70

10   ☐ $\div 10$ 10   ☐

30   ☐

☐   4

Dividing by 10

Share the number of chocolate chips between the **10** biscuits.

Write the answers. Try drawing the chocolate chips to help you.

10 chocolate chips

10 divided by **10** is [ ]

10 ÷ 10 = [ ]

20 chocolate chips

20 divided by **10** is [ ]

20 ÷ 10 = [ ]

30 chocolate chips

30 divided by **10** is [ ]

30 ÷ 10 = [ ]

40 chocolate chips

40 divided by **10** is [ ]

40 ÷ 10 = [ ]

50 chocolate chips

50 divided by **10** is [ ]

50 ÷ 10 = [ ]

60 chocolate chips

60 divided by **10** is [ ]

60 ÷ 10 = [ ]

70 chocolate chips

70 divided by **10** is [ ]

70 ÷ 10 = [ ]

80 chocolate chips

80 divided by **10** is [ ]

80 ÷ 10 = [ ]

90 chocolate chips

90 divided by **10** is [ ]

90 ÷ 10 = [ ]

100 chocolate chips

100 divided by **10** is [ ]

100 ÷ 10 = [ ]

110 chocolate chips

110 divided by **10** is [ ]

110 ÷ 10 = [ ]

120 chocolate chips

120 divided by **10** is [ ]

120 ÷ 10 = [ ]

Multiplying and dividing by 10

The machine is making cakes.

Write the missing numbers in the multiplication and division sentences.

$5 \times 10 = \boxed{}$

$\boxed{} \times 10 = 20$

$6 \times \boxed{} = 60$

$3 \times 10 = \boxed{}$

$8 \times \boxed{} = 80$

$\boxed{} \times 10 = 40$

$1 \times 10 = \boxed{}$

$\boxed{} \times 10 = 70$

$9 \times \boxed{} = 90$

$11 \times \boxed{} = 110$

$\boxed{} \times 10 = 120$

$10 \times \boxed{} = 80$

$10 \times \boxed{} = 60$

$90 \div 9 = \boxed{}$

$20 \div \boxed{} = 10$

$\boxed{} \times 5 = 50$

$10 \times 7 = \boxed{}$

$80 \div 10 = \boxed{}$

$40 \div \boxed{} = 10$

$10 \times 10 = \boxed{}$

Using ×10 table facts

Help the tractors round up the sheep. Find a number from a sheep to make the answer.

Write the answer on the tractor. Cross out the number you found.

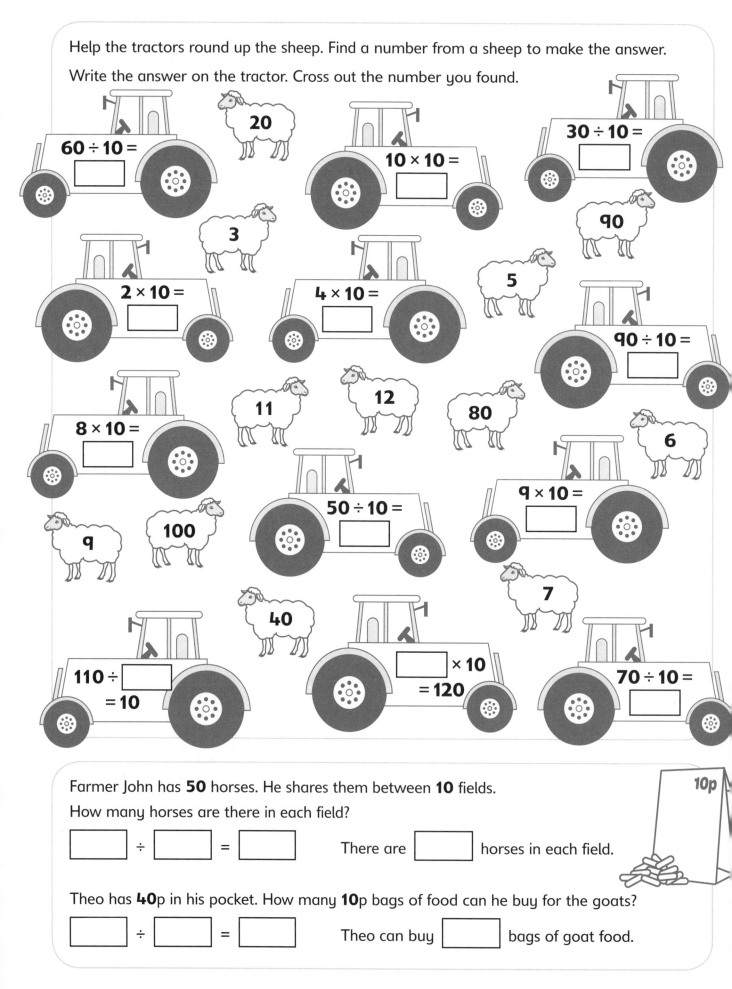

60 ÷ 10 =

20

10 × 10 =

30 ÷ 10 =

90

2 × 10 =

3

4 × 10 =

5

90 ÷ 10 =

8 × 10 =

11

12

80

6

9

100

50 ÷ 10 =

9 × 10 =

7

40

110 ÷ ⬜ = 10

⬜ × 10 = 120

70 ÷ 10 =

Farmer John has **50** horses. He shares them between **10** fields.

How many horses are there in each field?

⬜ ÷ ⬜ = ⬜   There are ⬜ horses in each field.

Theo has **40**p in his pocket. How many **10**p bags of food can he buy for the goats?

⬜ ÷ ⬜ = ⬜   Theo can buy ⬜ bags of goat food.

Solving problems

There are **10** hen houses in the field. There are **90** hens. The farmer puts equal numbers of hens into each house. How many hens live in each house?

In one week **6** hens lay **10** eggs each. How many eggs is that altogether?

The farmer now has **120** hens. There are still **10** hen houses. How many hens go into each house?

The farmer has **3** duck houses. **10** ducks sleep in each house. How many ducks are there altogether?

There are **40** cows on the farm. The farmer milks the cows **4** at a time. How many groups of **4** is that?

The farmer collects **7** litres of milk each day. How much milk does she collect in **10** days?

The sheep dog rounds up the sheep **5** at a time. He does this **10** times. How many sheep is that?

The farmer keeps **70** turkeys. The turkeys like to sleep **7** to each turkey house. How many turkey houses are there?

Solving mixed problems

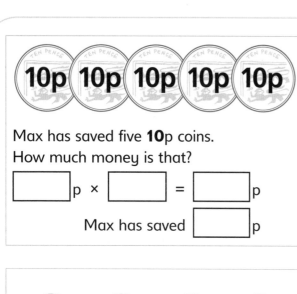
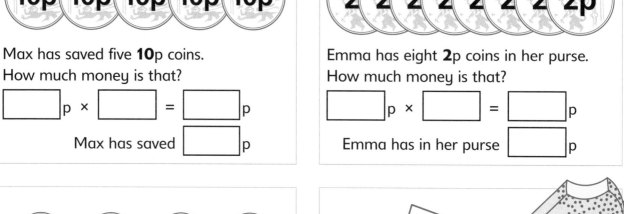

Max has saved five **10**p coins.
How much money is that?

[ ]p × [ ] = [ ]p

Max has saved [ ]p

Emma has eight **2**p coins in her purse.
How much money is that?

[ ]p × [ ] = [ ]p

Emma has in her purse [ ]p

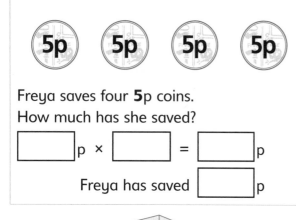

Freya saves four **5**p coins.
How much has she saved?

[ ]p × [ ] = [ ]p

Freya has saved [ ]p

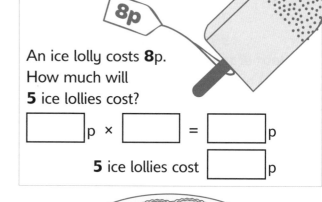

An ice lolly costs **8**p.
How much will
5 ice lollies cost?

[ ]p × [ ] = [ ]p

5 ice lollies cost [ ]p

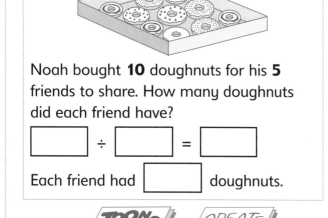

Noah bought **10** doughnuts for his **5**
friends to share. How many doughnuts
did each friend have?

[ ] ÷ [ ] = [ ]

Each friend had [ ] doughnuts.

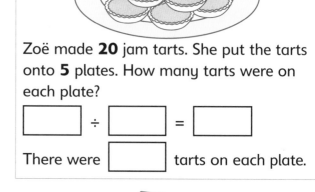

Zoë made **20** jam tarts. She put the tarts
onto **5** plates. How many tarts were on
each plate?

[ ] ÷ [ ] = [ ]

There were [ ] tarts on each plate.

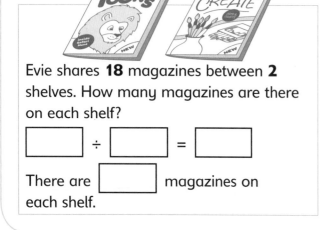

Evie shares **18** magazines between **2**
shelves. How many magazines are there
on each shelf?

[ ] ÷ [ ] = [ ]

There are [ ] magazines on
each shelf.

Sameer has **40**p in his pocket.
How many **10**p stickers can he buy?

[ ] ÷ [ ] = [ ]

Sameer can buy [ ] stickers.

Building the ×3 table

Count in **3**s. Write the missing numbers.

| 0 | 3 | 6 | ☐ | ☐ | ☐ | 18 | 21 | 24 | ☐ | ☐ | 33 | ☐ |

1 + 1 + 1 = ☐   **1** times **3** is ☐

2 + 2 + 2 = ☐   **2** times **3** is ☐

3 + 3 + 3 = ☐   **3** times **3** is ☐

4 + 4 + 4 = ☐   **4** times **3** is ☐

5 + 5 + 5 = ☐   **5** times **3** is ☐

6 + 6 + 6 = ☐   **6** times **3** is ☐

7 + 7 + 7 = ☐   **7** times **3** is ☐

8 + 8 + 8 = ☐   **8** times **3** is ☐

9 + 9 + 9 = ☐   **9** times **3** is ☐

10 + 10 + 10 = ☐   **10** times **3** is ☐

11 + 11 + 11 = ☐   **11** times **3** is ☐

12 + 12 + 12 = ☐   **12** times **3** is ☐

Multiplying by 3

Write the answers to these ×**3** questions.

In

2
5
7
3
12
6
1
8
10
9
4
11

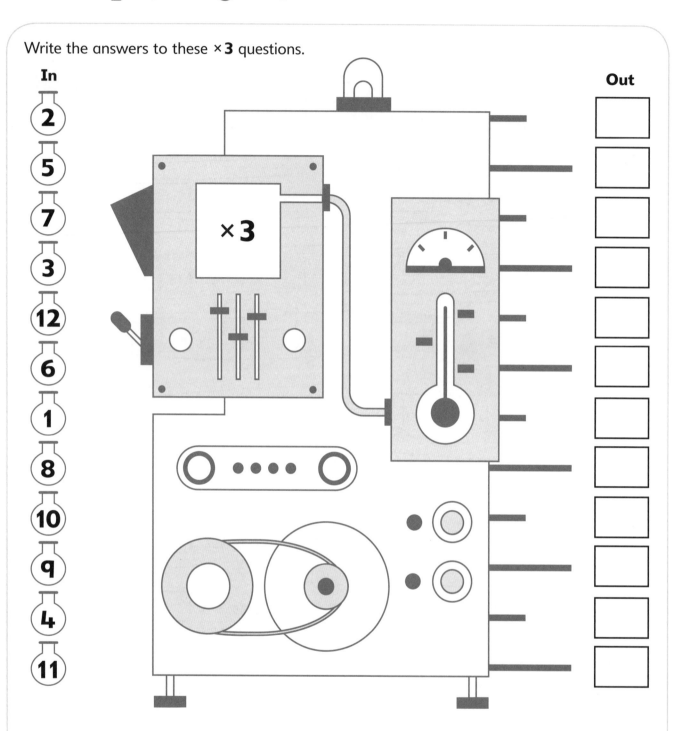

×**3**

Out

Write three more ×**3** table facts with odd answers in the Odd column.

Write three more ×**3** table facts with even answers in the Even column.

Remember:

Odd times odd gives odd numbers.

Even times odd gives even numbers.

Odd answer	Even answer
3 × 5 = 15	3 × 8 = 24

Dividing by 3

Use the pictures to help you. Write the answers to these division questions.

3 cakes shared between **3** boxes is ☐ each.

3 divided by **3** is ☐   **3 ÷ 3 =** ☐

6 cakes shared between **3** boxes is ☐ each.

6 divided by **3** is ☐   **6 ÷ 3 =** ☐

9 cakes shared between **3** boxes is ☐ each.

9 divided by **3** is ☐   **9 ÷ 3 =** ☐

12 cakes shared between **3** boxes is ☐ each.

12 divided by **3** is ☐   **12 ÷ 3 =** ☐

15 cakes shared between **3** boxes is ☐ each.

15 divided by **3** is ☐   **15 ÷ 3 =** ☐

18 cakes shared between **3** boxes is ☐ each.

18 divided by **3** is ☐   **18 ÷ 3 =** ☐

21 cakes shared between **3** boxes is ☐ each.

21 divided by **3** is ☐   **21 ÷ 3 =** ☐

24 cakes shared between **3** boxes is ☐ each.

24 divided by **3** is ☐   **24 ÷ 3 =** ☐

Dividing by 3

Use the pictures to help you. Write the answers to these division questions.

Each set of shells is shared between **3** buckets.

27 shells shared between **3** buckets

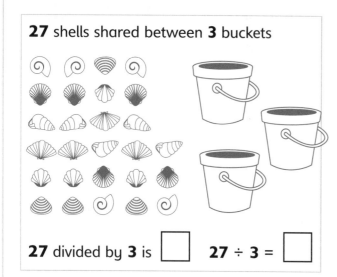

27 divided by **3** is ☐   **27 ÷ 3 =** ☐

30 shells shared between **3** buckets

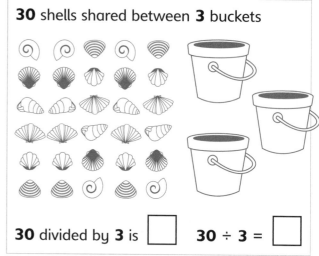

30 divided by **3** is ☐   **30 ÷ 3 =** ☐

33 shells shared between **3** buckets

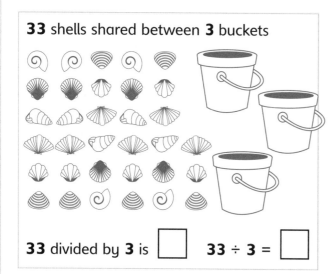

33 divided by **3** is ☐   **33 ÷ 3 =** ☐

36 shells shared between **3** buckets

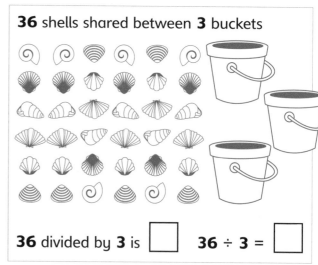

36 divided by **3** is ☐   **36 ÷ 3 =** ☐

Tom finds **15** starfish. He shares them equally between **3** buckets.

How many starfish go into each bucket? ☐

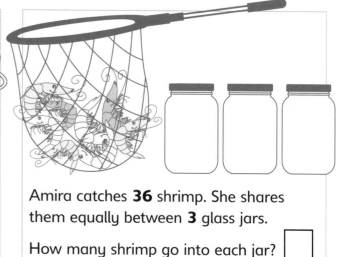

Amira catches **36** shrimp. She shares them equally between **3** glass jars.

How many shrimp go into each jar? ☐

Multiplying and dividing by 3

You know these facts...   ...so you can find these facts!

7 × 3 = 21   21 ÷ 3 = 7   3 × 7 = 21   21 ÷ 7 = 3

Draw a line to match the question to its answer.

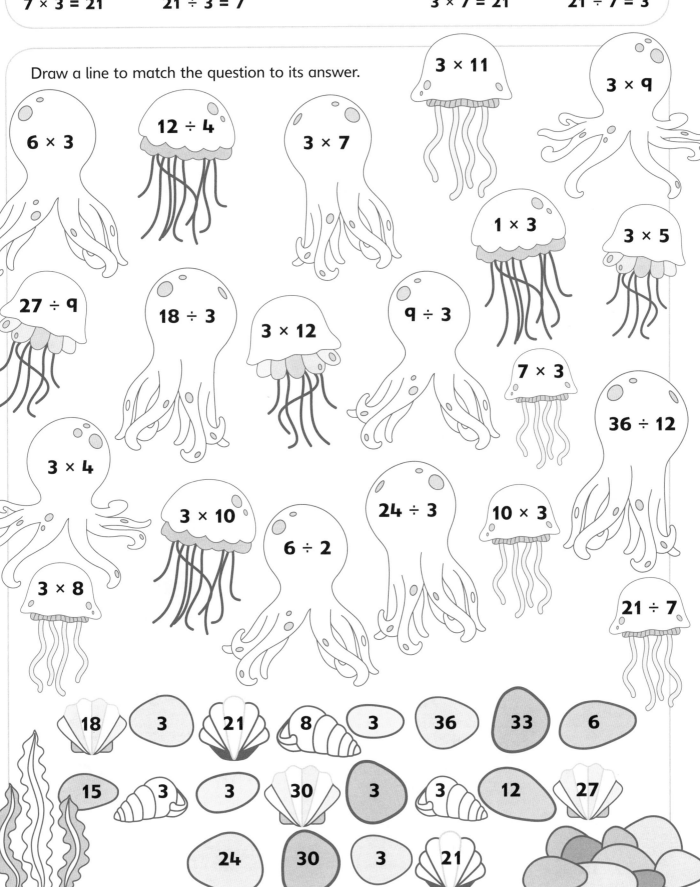

6 × 3

12 ÷ 4

3 × 7

3 × 11

3 × 9

1 × 3

3 × 5

27 ÷ 9

18 ÷ 3

3 × 12

9 ÷ 3

7 × 3

36 ÷ 12

3 × 4

3 × 10

6 ÷ 2

24 ÷ 3

10 × 3

3 × 8

21 ÷ 7

18   3   21   8   3   36   33   6

15   3   3   30   3   3   12   27

24   30   3   21

Using ×3 table facts

Read the questions on the pirates.

Draw lines to the answers on the treasure.

21 ÷ 3

30

5

9 ÷ 3

12 ÷ 4

10

3

18

6 × 3

5 × 3

8 × 3

6

3 × 7

27

6

24 ÷ 3

12

10 × 3

3

6 ÷ 3

21

8

3 ÷ 3

9

1 × 3

27 ÷ 9

15 ÷ 3

2

7

1

24

4 × 3

18 ÷ 3

30 ÷ 3

3 × 3

3

2 × 3

3

3 × 9

15

Solving problems

Read the word problem. Write the answer.

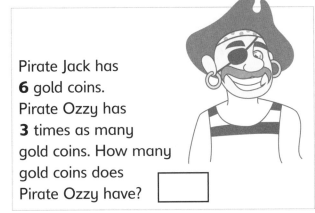

Pirate Jack has
6 gold coins.
Pirate Ozzy has
3 times as many
gold coins. How many
gold coins does
Pirate Ozzy have?

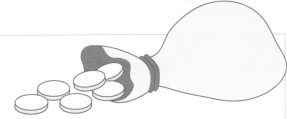

Pirate Ozzy spends some of his gold
coins. Now he has **15** gold coins.
He shares the coins between **5** purses.
How many gold coins
are there in each purse?

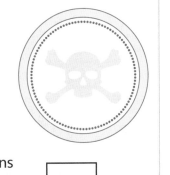

Pirate Ben has
36 gold coins.
He shares the
coins between
himself and his
two brothers.
How many gold coins
do they each have now?

Pirate Ozzy steals
some gold coins.
Now he has **24** coins.
He puts equal numbers
of coins into **8** gold cups.
How many coins
are in each cup?

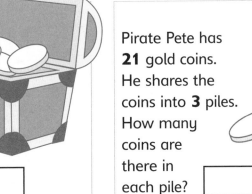

Pirate Jon has
3 gold coins.
His brother
Pirate Rusty
has **6** times
as many gold coins.
How many coins
does Pirate Rusty have?

Pirate Pete has
21 gold coins.
He shares the
coins into **3** piles.
How many
coins are
there in
each pile?

Cabin boy
Steve has
just **2**
gold coins.
Pirate Sam
says he has **3** times as many
coins as Steve. How many
coins does Pirate Sam have?

The parrot has
18 gold coins.
He puts them into
piles of **6** coins.
How many
piles of coins
does the
parrot make?

Multiplying and dividing by 2, 3, 5 and 10

Look at these function machines.

Write what is happening in the box.

The first one is done for you.

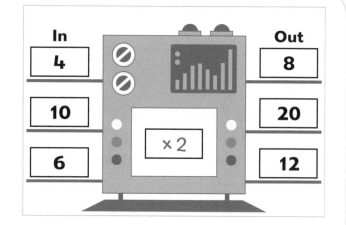

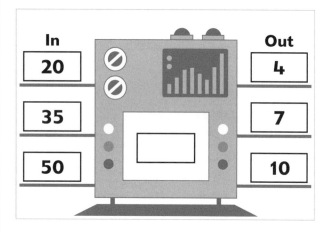

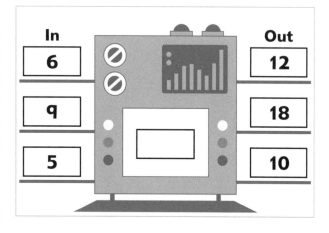

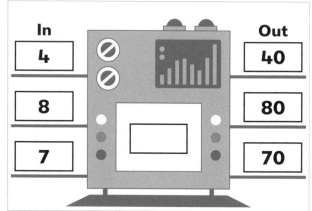

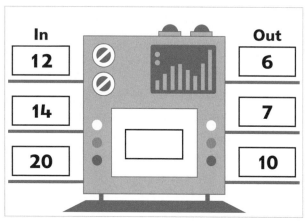

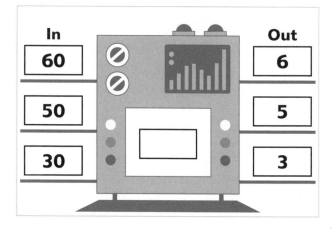

Building the ×4 table

Count in **4**s. Write the missing numbers.

0	4	8	12	☐	☐	☐	28	32	☐	☐	☐	☐
☐	☐	☐	12	16	☐	☐	☐	☐	☐	☐	☐	48

1 + 1 + 1 + 1 = ☐   1 times **4** is ☐

2 + 2 + 2 + 2 = ☐   2 times **4** is ☐

3 + 3 + 3 + 3 = ☐   3 times **4** is ☐

4 + 4 + 4 + 4 = ☐   4 times **4** is ☐

5 + 5 + 5 + 5 = ☐   5 times **4** is ☐

6 + 6 + 6 + 6 = ☐   6 times **4** is ☐

7 + 7 + 7 + 7 = ☐   7 times **4** is ☐

8 + 8 + 8 + 8 = ☐   8 times **4** is ☐

9 + 9 + 9 + 9 = ☐   9 times **4** is ☐

10 + 10 + 10 + 10 = ☐   10 times **4** is ☐

11 + 11 + 11 + 11 = ☐   11 times **4** is ☐

12 + 12 + 12 + 12 = ☐   12 times **4** is ☐

Multiplying by 4

If you are not sure of the answers try doubling the ×**2** fact.

So: **3** × **2** = **6** and **3** × **4** = **12**. **12** is double **6**.

Write the answers to these multiplications.

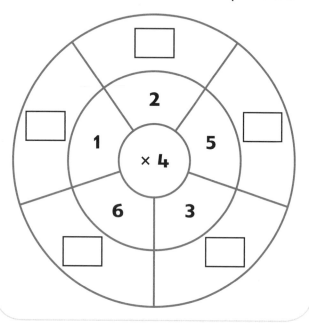

Write the answers to these multiplications.

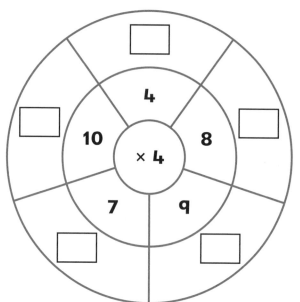

Here are some answers to the ×**4** table.

Match each answer to its multiplication.

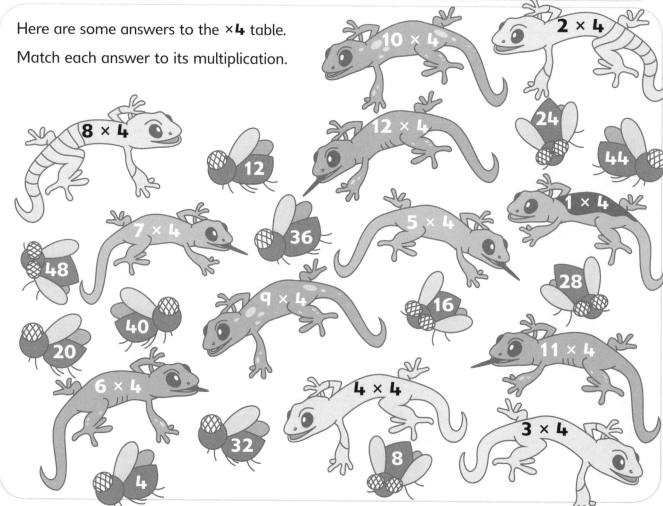

Dividing by 4

Use the pictures to help you.

Write the answers to these division questions.

4 beetles shared between **4** leaves is

☐ each.

4 divided by **4** is ☐   **4 ÷ 4 =** ☐

---

8 beetles shared between **4** leaves is

☐ each.

8 divided by **4** is ☐   **8 ÷ 4 =** ☐

---

12 beetles shared between **4** leaves is

☐ each.

12 divided by **4** is ☐   **12 ÷ 4 =** ☐

---

16 beetles shared between **4** leaves is

☐ each.

16 divided by **4** is ☐   **16 ÷ 4 =** ☐

---

20 beetles shared between **4** leaves is

☐ each.

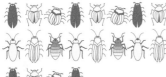

20 divided by **4** is ☐   **20 ÷ 4 =** ☐

---

24 beetles shared between **4** leaves is

☐ each.

24 divided by **4** is ☐   **24 ÷ 4 =** ☐

---

28 beetles shared between **4** leaves is

☐ each.

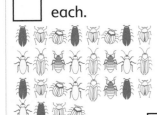

28 divided by **4** is ☐   **28 ÷ 4 =** ☐

---

32 beetles shared between **4** leaves is

☐ each.

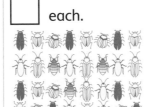

32 divided by **4** is ☐   **32 ÷ 4 =** ☐

Dividing by 4

Use the pictures to help you.

Write the answers to these division questions.

36 slugs shared between **4** lettuces is ☐

36 divided by **4** is ☐   **36 ÷ 4 =** ☐

40 slugs shared between **4** lettuces is ☐

40 divided by **4** is ☐   **40 ÷ 4 =** ☐

44 slugs shared between **4** lettuces is ☐

44 divided by **4** is ☐   **44 ÷ 4 =** ☐

48 slugs shared between **4** lettuces is ☐

48 divided by **4** is ☐   **48 ÷ 4 =** ☐

24 ladybirds sit on a bush. There are **4** ladybirds on a leaf. How many leaves have ladybirds on them? ☐

44 ladybirds settle on another bush. They settle equally on **11** leaves. How many ladybirds are there on each leaf? ☐

38

Multiplying and dividing by 4

You know these facts...

$6 \times 4 = 24$ $24 \div 4 = 6$

...so you can work these facts!

$4 \times 6 = 24$ $24 \div 6 = 4$

Match the multiplication to its answer.

Write the answers to these division questions.

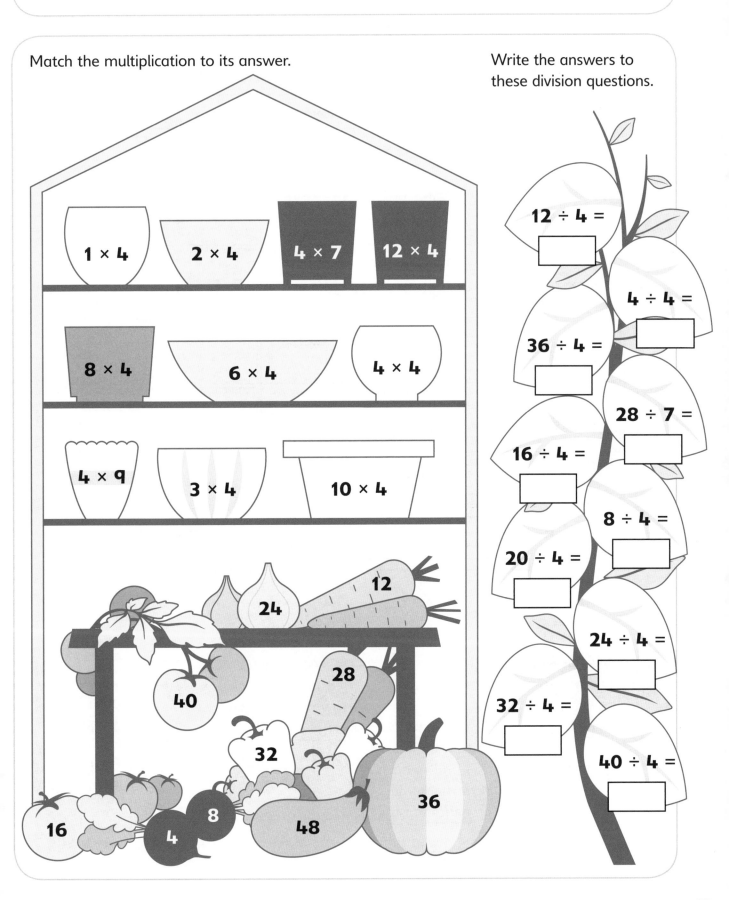

1×4 2×4 4×7 12×4

8×4 6×4 4×4

4×9 3×4 10×4

12   24   40   28   32   16   8   4   48   36

$12 \div 4 =$

$4 \div 4 =$

$36 \div 4 =$

$28 \div 7 =$

$16 \div 4 =$

$8 \div 4 =$

$20 \div 4 =$

$24 \div 4 =$

$32 \div 4 =$

$40 \div 4 =$

Using ×4 table facts

Write the answers in the boxes.

$36 \div 4 = \boxed{}$

$6 \times 4 = \boxed{}$

$1 \times 4 = \boxed{}$

$4 \div 4 = \boxed{}$

$9 \times 4 = \boxed{}$

$4 \times 4 = \boxed{}$

$12 \div 4 = \boxed{}$

$4 \times 1 = \boxed{}$

$2 \times 4 = \boxed{}$

$8 \times 4 = \boxed{}$

$20 \div 4 = \boxed{}$

$8 \div 4 = \boxed{}$

$28 \div 4 = \boxed{}$

$16 \div 4 = \boxed{}$

$3 \times 4 = \boxed{}$

$4 \times 8 = \boxed{}$

$24 \div 4 = \boxed{}$

$40 \div 4 = \boxed{}$

$32 \div 4 = \boxed{}$

$5 \times 4 = \boxed{}$

$48 \div 4 = \boxed{}$

$7 \times 4 = \boxed{}$

$10 \times 4 = \boxed{}$

Morgan has **40**p. How many **4**p pipe cleaners can he buy?

$\boxed{}$

Ava wants **5** pencils. The pencils are **4**p each. How much will the pencils cost?

$\boxed{}$p

There are **4** felt tips in a pack. How many felt tips are there in **6** packs?

$\boxed{}$

Lucy wants to share **32** sequins between **8** cards. How many sequins will there be on each card?

$\boxed{}$

Solving problems

Write the answers to the word problems.

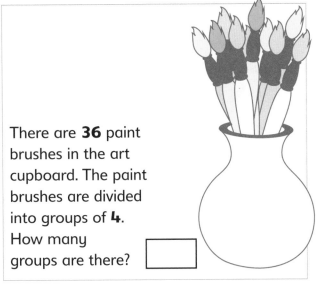

There are **36** paint brushes in the art cupboard. The paint brushes are divided into groups of **4**. How many groups are there?

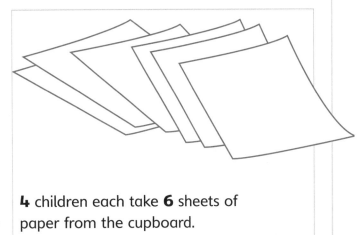

4 children each take **6** sheets of paper from the cupboard. How many sheets of paper is that in total?

There are **28** chairs put around **7** tables. How many chairs are around each table?

24 of the children work in groups of **6**. Each group paints a large tree picture. How many trees will be painted?

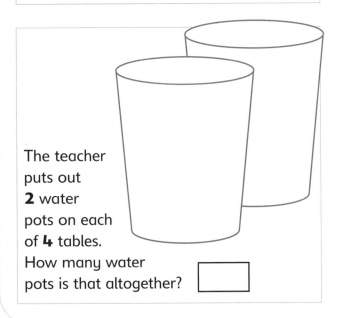

The teacher puts out **2** water pots on each of **4** tables. How many water pots is that altogether?

48 pictures are painted. The teacher puts them on the wall in groups of **12**. How many groups are there?

Multiplying and dividing by 3 and 4

Use the numbers **3**, **4** and **12**.

Write two multiplication and two division sentences.

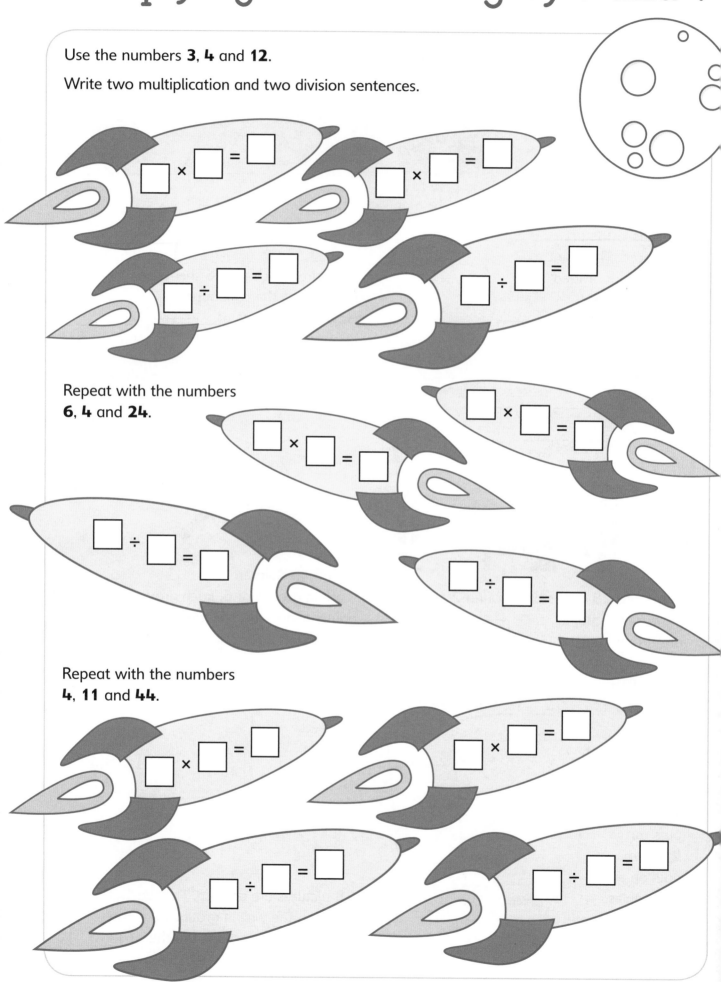

$$\square \times \square = \square$$

$$\square \times \square = \square$$

$$\square \div \square = \square$$

$$\square \div \square = \square$$

Repeat with the numbers
6, **4** and **24**.

$$\square \times \square = \square$$

$$\square \times \square = \square$$

$$\square \div \square = \square$$

$$\square \div \square = \square$$

Repeat with the numbers
4, **11** and **44**.

$$\square \times \square = \square$$

$$\square \times \square = \square$$

$$\square \div \square = \square$$

$$\square \div \square = \square$$

Schofield & Sims Times Tables Practice 1

Multiplying and dividing by 3 and 4

Join the answer to the problem with a line.

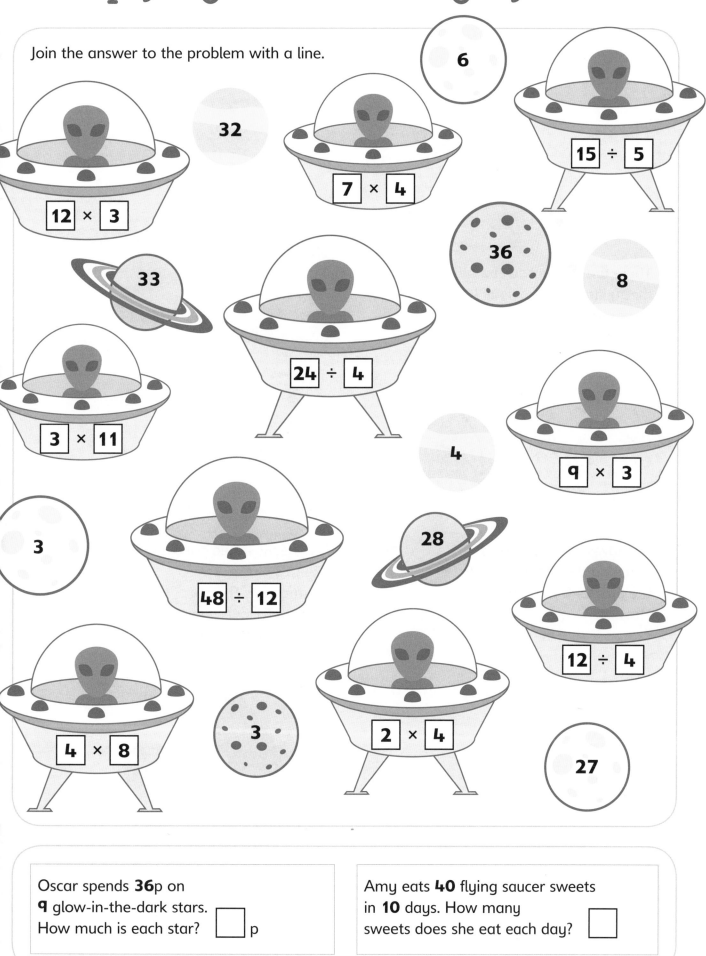

6

$15 \div 5$

32

7×4

12×3

36

8

33

$24 \div 4$

3×11

4

9×3

3

28

$48 \div 12$

$12 \div 4$

4×8

3

2×4

27

Oscar spends **36**p on
9 glow-in-the-dark stars.
How much is each star? ☐ p

Amy eats **40** flying saucer sweets
in **10** days. How many
sweets does she eat each day? ☐

Solving mixed problems

Write the answers to these word problems.

There are **24** sunflowers. Alfie plants the sunflowers in rows of **4**.
How many rows does Alfie plant? ☐

Nyasha picks **3** flowers to go in a vase. She does this **7** times.
How many flowers does she pick? ☐

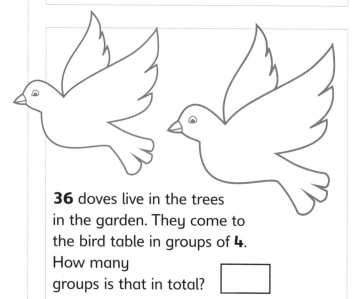

36 doves live in the trees in the garden. They come to the bird table in groups of **4**.
How many groups is that in total? ☐

The newts in the pond like to swim in **2**s. Liam counts **9** pairs of newts. How many newts is that in total? ☐

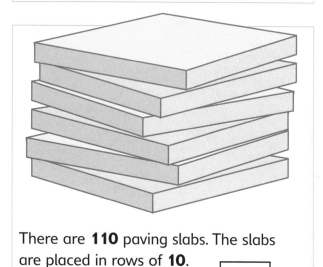

There are **110** paving slabs. The slabs are placed in rows of **10**.
How many rows are there? ☐

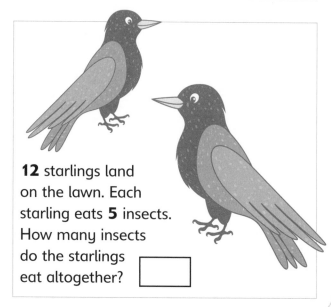

12 starlings land on the lawn. Each starling eats **5** insects. How many insects do the starlings eat altogether? ☐

Solving mixed problems

7 spiders build a web each.
3 flies land on each web.
How many flies are
on the webs in total? ☐

Finn puts
2 handfuls of
birdseed on
the bird table.
He does this
every day.
In one week
how many
handfuls of
seed go
onto the
bird table? ☐

Bird Food

There are **35** daisies on the lawn.
Emilia picks **7** daisies and makes
a chain with them. How many
times can she do this in total? ☐

The gardener finds **55** snails.
He shares the snails between
11 saucers. How many
snails are on each saucer? ☐

Maryam picks up **7** leaves.
She does this **5** times in total.
How many leaves does
Maryam pick up altogether? ☐

In the shed there
are **40** flowerpots.
The gardener puts
the flowerpots
in stacks of **10**.
How many
stacks of
flowerpots
does the
gardener make? ☐

What I know

Use your times tables to escape with the treasure – try not to get caught!

6 × 10 =

3 × 11 =

21 ÷ 7 =

6 ÷ 3 =

6 × 5 =

24 ÷ 8 =

80 ÷ 8 =

4 × 9 =

2 × 12 =

10 × 10 =

36 ÷ 4 =

4 ÷ 4 =

27 ÷ 3 =

36 ÷ 3 =

9 × 11 =

24 ÷ 3 =

5 × 8 =

24 ÷ 6 =

7 × 5 =

10 × 4 =

Multiplication table

This is a multiplication table.

Write in the answers to the times tables as you learn them.
Remember: you know **8 × 5** so you can find **5 × 8**, and so on.

The grey boxes are table facts that you don't know yet.

×	1	2	3	4	5	6	7	8	9	10	11	12
1												
2												
3												
4												
5												
6												
7												
8												
9												
10												
11												
12												

If you forget a division fact such as **32 ÷ 4**, find **32** in the chart and look along the row and column to find **8** and **4**. So **32 ÷ 4 = 8**.

It's time for **Times Tables Practice 2**.

Well done!

Schofield&Sims

the long-established educational publisher specialising in maths, English and science

Knowing the times tables is vital to success in maths. **Times Tables Practice** gives children extensive practice in all the times tables relevant to their age group, providing enjoyable activities with attractive illustrations that will hold their attention throughout. All the activities have been devised to support the National Curriculum.

Times Tables Practice 1 covers the ×2, ×3, ×4, ×5 and ×10 times tables.

The activities are structured in sections that look separately at different tables. Each section encourages children to:

• practise counting
• build the multiplication table
• memorise and manipulate number facts
• improve their rapid recall skills
• derive related division facts.

Many exercises in the book include notes highlighting useful rules that will help children to remember their tables. Children are also prompted to use known facts learned earlier in the book to help them tackle more challenging multiplication and division questions. Once they have mastered each table, problem-solving pages incorporating everyday themes, including money, encourage them to apply their new-found skills to real-life situations.

The book ends with number problems, 'What I know' and multiplication table pages designed to reinforce learning and build confidence, preparing children for classroom testing.

The titles in this series are as follows:

Times Tables Practice 1   ISBN 978 07217 1373 1
Times Tables Practice 2   ISBN 978 07217 1374 8

Have you tried **Times Tables Tests** by Schofield & Sims?
This series of books helps to secure children's knowledge and application of essential multiplication and division facts and develop their understanding of number vocabulary.

ISBN 978 07217 1373 1
Key Stages 1 & 2
Age range 6–8 years
£3.50 (Retail price)

ISBN 978-07217-1373-1

9 780721 713731 >

For further information and to place your order visit
www.schofieldandsims.co.uk or telephone 01484 607080